The Locked Room

Michael Thomson

Oxford University Press

The Locked Room:
a Tale of Murder

How to read this book

You are a well-known detective. You have been called in to find out about a death. It could be murder. You need to find out these things:

- Why it was done (the Motive)
- How it was done (the Method)
- When it was done (the Opportunity)

and when you have worked these out:

- Who did it (The Murderer).

You can write down what you think for each of these. You will be given your own copy of the 'Who Did It?' sheet on page 3. If you want to change your mind as you read the story, just write it down as your next guess.

You are the main person in this story. To read it, you start at number 1. Then you will choose to go to other places (numbers). Read or do what is asked when you reach each place.

Who Did It?

A good time to fill in your ideas is after you have read number 18. You can also try it after you have finished number 10.

Write down who you think did the murder. Write down what you think for the other things as well.

	Guess 1	Guess 2	Guess 3
The Murderer (Who?):			
The Motive (Why?):			
The Method (How?):			
The Opportunity (When?):			

The Locked Room

1

You have been called by the police to Bigwell House in the country. It is the manor house where Lord Framwell lives. Well, he does not live there now. He is dead. The Lord's death is what you are here to look into.

You look up at the large house. It is two storeys high. It looks like the set of a horror film: spooky and old. You notice that there are tall, wide chimneys on the roof.

Lord Framwell was found dead in his bedroom. The odd part is that the door was locked and bolted from the *inside*. The room is on the second floor and the window was also locked from the inside. The local police say that there was no other way in.

Framwell seems to have had a heart attack. The local police are not so sure. It might have been murder. But the room was locked. So how was he killed?

You ring the bell at the big front door. A tall, thin butler lets you in. He looks down his nose at you.

You can talk to the butler – go to 9, or you can ask to look at the room where Framwell was found dead – go to 13.

2

Simon is pacing up and down the garden. He is a fit-looking young man. He tells you that he has just returned from the Andes. 'I nearly met my own death,' he says, 'climbing all those rockfaces. Still, I got Uncle Martin's silly frog. Yellow-green, with a darker belly and red back legs. He'd been after a frog like that for years. I put it in the glass case with holes in it. Uncle

told me to keep it closed up. Something to do with damp air. Wouldn't have wanted to touch it anyway!'

Simon goes on and on. He shows no sadness and yet his father has just been killed. You mention this and he tells you that he hated his father. 'He beat mother, you know,' he says. 'He has done for years. I could do nothing when I was a child, but now... He hit her again yesterday. He said the food at dinner tasted funny. We shouted at each other. I told him not to touch her again.'

Simon walks off towards the house, clenching his fists. Go to 15.

3

Lord Framwell's doctor says that he did not die from a heart attack. 'It was a nerve toxin,' he says. 'It would have made his muscles stop working. That means he would stop breathing and his heart would go into shock. How the toxin got into him, I do not know. Could have been in something he ate. Maybe it was a gas, but if so the others in the house would also have been affected.' Go to 12.

4

You visit the family solicitor. He tells you that Lord Framwell's Will left the Estate to his brother. 'There was no love lost between them,' he says. 'But I think Lord Framwell felt bad because he was the Lord and his twin brother had nothing.'

The solicitor also says he does not know of any other Will. Go to 17.

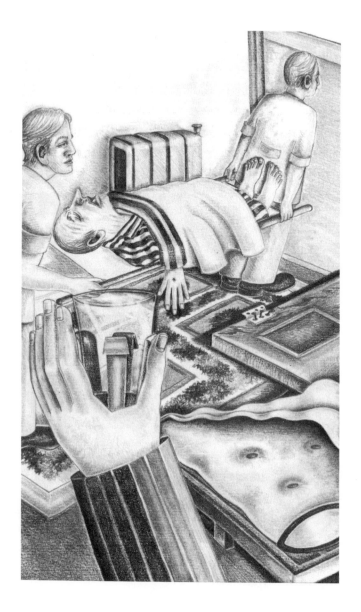

5

You get the body taken away to find out how Lord Framwell died. You notice a red mark on his hand as the body is removed.

You send the glass and its dregs to the lab. The results of the tests on the body and the dregs in the glass will take a day to come back.

Now if you have not talked to the butler – go to 9. If you have, you can talk to the others in the house – go to 15. If you have talked to everyone – go to 12.

6

You return to Lord Framwell's room and go to the fire place. You look into the grate and find some burnt paper. You can make out the word 'Will', but that is all. You look up the chimney. It is blocked. No room for anyone to climb down. The logs are just for show.

You look all round the floor and you find a small hole in the skirting board. You go into the next door room. You notice another hole that joins with the one in Lord Framwell's bedroom. You find a glass tank full of water. There is water spilt on the floor and the room is very damp.

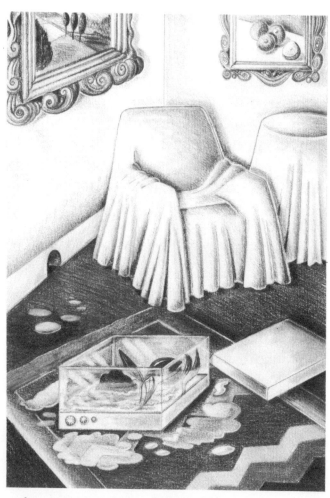

As you go out past Lord Framwell's bedroom you notice that his door has a gap under it. It is a few centimetres wide. Go to 12.

7

You find Lady Framwell in her room. She is looking pale and says she is tired from making dinner. She has a black eye. She does not say how she got it. You ask her to tell you what went on the night before. She starts to laugh and cry at the same time. 'I'm free of him at last!' she sobs and then puts her hand to her mouth. She looks at you with dark eyes.

She tells you that after dinner Lord Framwell spent a little time talking to their son. She does not say anything about being hit or Simon and her husband shouting. Then Lord Framwell went to bed. She tells you that he always locked the door as it was a habit he had got into when he was travelling in Japan.

'That is also where he got the low bed. It is called a "futon",' she says. 'Giles, the butler, took him his evening drink as he always did. Poor Giles. He is such a nice man. I'm afraid my husband was going to sack him. He said that he was going to make sure Giles never got a job again.'

You ask her what is in the room next to Lord Framwell's. She says, 'Oh, just a spare room. We never use it. It has no heating and is always so cold. Not like the rest of the house. It's been like an oven this last week.' Go to 15.

8

The Lab tells you that the glass had drinking chocolate in it, nothing else. The leftovers from the dinner were also fine – just not very well cooked! Go to 12.

9

You talk to the butler in the kitchen. He tells you that there are only three others living in the house. 'Cook is on holiday and we do not have a maid at present. Master Simon, Lord Framwell's son, is staying. He has just come back from South America. He is a mountain climber. He won't stay long. He hated his father. In fact, they were shouting at each other last night. Lady Framwell is here, of course. She is in her room in a state of shock.

She is also rather tired after making dinner last night. Mr Martin, Lord Framwell's brother, is also here. He lives in the West Wing, with his frogs.'

'Frogs?' you say.

'Yes, frogs,' the butler sneers. 'He collects them. He has many kinds from all over the world.'

Just then the doorbell rings. The butler says that he must go as it is the central heating man. It seems that the heating is playing up. It has been too hot in the house for the last few days.

Now you can go and look at the room where Framwell died – go to 13. Or you can talk to the others – go to 15.

10

At the end of the first day you make some notes.

The Murderer (Who?)??

Motive (Why?)

1. Lady Framwell - her husband bullied her.
2. Simon – hated father for bullying his mother.
3. Butler - might lose his job.
4. Martin - wanted to be Lord.

Method (How?)

1. Something in the drink or maybe in dinner (wife or butler).
2. Way in over the roof and down chimney (son can climb).

Opportunity (When)

At night while he was asleep or just before.

You also think about some odd things. Why did Martin show you a blue-green frog when Simon said he had given him a yellow-green one with red back legs? Has the heat anything to do with it all? You get the leftovers from the dinner out of the dustbin. You send them to the Lab.

You can now use your 'Who Did It?' sheet to fill in your ideas. Make a note of the number 10 so that you can come back here and read on. If you prefer, you can just carry on reading and go to 12.

11

You find Martin Framwell in the West Wing. It is linked to the main house by a passageway. Martin is in a room full of glass tanks. Inside the tanks are rocks, earth, plants, little pools of water, and lots of frogs!

Martin looks just like Lord Framwell!! It turns out that he is the twin of his Lordship. 'Yes,' he says, 'my brother was born ten minutes before I was. He got to be "Lord Framwell" when our father died. I got nothing.'

Martin turns away and starts to mess with

some controls. 'You have to get the heat just right for them. Not too hot and lots of damp in the air.'

He is looking at a frog that is blue-green all over. 'Nice of him to bring it back from the Andes for me. Rare. I've wanted it for years.'

He says he heard nothing the night of his brother's death. Go to 15.

12

You should have talked to the butler, Lady Framwell, Martin Framwell, and Simon Framwell. You should also have been to Lord Framwell's room. If you have not – go to 15. If you have – go to 10 where you will find some useful notes.

You spend the next day finding out more! You need to know *how* Lord Framwell died first of all. You can:

• Go and talk to the doctor and find out how Lord Framwell died – go to 3.

• Look at the room where he died, inch by inch – go to 6.

• Find out what was in the glass and in the dinner – go to 8.

When you have been to 3, 6, and 8 you can go on to 17.

13

You go up to the first-floor bedroom. The door has been broken open from the outside. The butler tells you that Lord Framwell's son did this. The door has been pushed out of its frame with great strength. There was no way in without the door being smashed down.

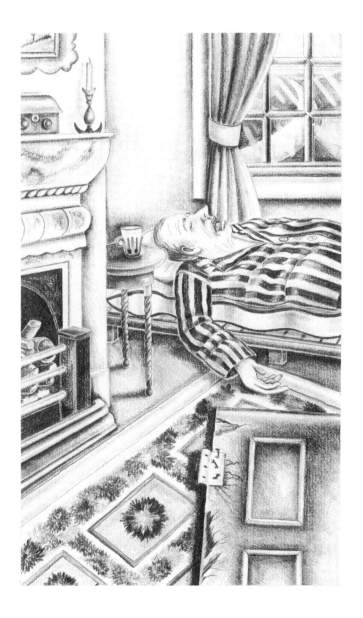

You go in and check the windows. They are locked. You can see that no other part of the house overlooks this room. No one could have seen in or fired something in. The window is not broken. You see:

• A low bed on the floor.

• A glass with the dregs of something in it by the bed.

• A wide fire place with unburnt logs. Above it is one of the tall chimneys.

Lord Framwell's body lies across the bed. His face is twisted. He must have died in great pain. The doctor has said that it looked like a heart attack. Framwell was a man in his fifties, rather unfit and plump. It could well have been a heart attack or something made to look like a heart attack.

If you can send the body and the glass away for checking – go to 5. If you have not talked to the butler – go to 9.

14

You visit the Frog House at London Zoo. You ask about frogs from South America. You go over to one with a yellow-green back, darker belly and red back legs. 'That is *Dendrobates*

23

Terribilis!' says the Keeper. 'We have to wear rubber gloves to touch it. If you touch its skin a nerve toxin can get into your body. It stops your heart!'

It is very damp in the room. 'These frogs like the damp,' says the Keeper. 'They can tell if the air is dry and always head for the damp air or wetness.' Go to 17.

15

You can talk to Simon, the Lord's son – go to 2; to Martin Framwell, his brother – go to 11; or to Lady Framwell, his wife – go to 7.

You can look at the room where Framwell died – go to 13; or talk to the butler – go to 9. If you have done all these you can go to 12.

16

You track down the cook at home. She is not much help at first. Then she tells you that she was a witness to Lord Framwell's new Will. 'He changed it. He was going to leave all the Estate to his son, Simon. He said he did not see why he should let his brother have it all – the lazy good-for-nothing.' Go to 17.

17

Now you need to find out more about *why* Lord Framwell was murdered. What would be left behind after he died and did anyone else know anything? You can:

• Find the cook and talk to her – go to 16.

• Talk to the family solicitor about Lord Framwell's Will – go to 4.

Something else still nags at you. You need to find out all you can. You decide to go to London Zoo to find out about frogs. Go to 14.

When you have been to 16, 4, and 14 you can move on to 18.

18

You now call everyone to the study. You are going to solve the murder.

First, check you have been to all the places you are asked to at 12 and 17. Then come back here to 18.

Now that you have been everywhere, you can solve the murder. Write down what you think happened. Do this by filling in your 'Who Did It?' sheet. If you have already made a guess, you can change your ideas if you wish. The notes at 10 might help.

Now go to 19.

19

You call the butler, Lady Framwell, Simon Framwell, and Martin Framwell to the study. When you tell them that they all had motives for killing Lord Framwell they get angry.

'But someone had a greater motive than the rest,' you say. 'Someone who knew that Lord Framwell had changed his Will. Someone who would no longer gain the Estate should his Lordship die.'

Martin jumps up. 'Yes! It's true I did know that my brother was changing his Will to keep

me out of it. He told me. He gloated, in fact. I may have burnt the new Will, but you can't prove I murdered him!'

You go on, 'Why was it so hot those few nights? Why was the room next door to his Lordship's so damp? Martin had broken the central heating. He knew that it would be hot and dry in the house. Night after night he slipped a frog under the door of his brother's room.'

Simon starts to giggle at this. The butler smirks. The others look at you as if you have gone mad. You take no notice.

'He made a small hole between the two rooms. The frog, feeling that it was cool and damp next door, went into the hole.'

'What a crazy story!' Martin says. 'But even if it was true, so what?'

'What the murderer hoped was that the frog would touch his Lordship as it hopped about. If it did, his Lordship would die, as the frog was none other than *Dendrobates Terriblis!* Just one touch from this frog will kill you because of its deadly nerve toxin. The skin of the frog gives off slime with the toxin in. The hotter it is, the more slime is made! At last, on one

night the frog did touch Lord Framwell. He died and the frog hopped into the cool, damp room as it had every other night! So, no murder weapon!

We have found the frog and a bill of sale made out to you, Martin Framwell, to import the frog as a well-known dealer. You used Simon to bring in the frog from South America, knowing he knew nothing about what you planned!'

As Martin is arrested by the police, he shouts, 'Ten minutes, that was the only difference between us! Ten minutes. I should have been Lord Framwell!'

Oxford University Press, Great Clarendon Street,
Oxford, OX2 6DP

Oxford   New York
Athens   Auckland   Bangkok   Bogota   Bombay
Buenos Aires   Calcutta   Cape Town   Dar es Salaam
Delhi   Florence   Hong Kong   Istanbul   Karachi
Kuala Lumpur   Madras   Madrid   Melbourne
Mexico City   Nairobi   Paris   Singapore
Taipei   Tokyo   Toronto

and associated companies in
Berlin   Ibadan

Oxford is a trade mark of Oxford University Press

© Michael Thomson 1995
First published 1995
Reprinted 1996, 1997   .

ISBN 0 19 833499 0

Printed in Great Britain

Illustrations by Susan Sluglett